P9-CEB-128

JANE ADDAMS
WORLD NEIGHBOR

JANE ADDAMS

WORLD NEIGHBOR

MIRIAM GILBERT

Illustrated by Corinne Boyd Dillon

New York ABINGDON PRESS *Nashville*

PRINTED IN THE UNITED STATES OF AMERICA

▲

LIBRARY OF CONGRESS CATALOG NUMBER: 60-5319

To My Three Mothers:

My Mother
My Stepmother
My Mother-in-law

CONTENTS

CHAPTER I

• THE RICH AND POOR •

Jane frowned at herself in her bedroom mirror. "Ugly, ugly, ugly!" she said angrily to her thin face. "You are the plainest little girl I have ever seen."

"Jennie," Polly, the housekeeper, called, using the family nickname for Jane, "your father will be ready to take you to Sunday school in a few minutes. Please hurry."

"When Sunday school is over," Jane decided, "I will go down the stairs as fast as I can. Father is always busy after church with the students in his Bible class or visitors from out of town. I will ask my uncle if I may walk home with him, the way I did last week. Maybe then no one will know that I belong to the handsome Mr. Addams."

"Jennie," Polly called again, "what are you mooning about?"

Jane stared at herself again from the bottom of her turned-in toes to the top of her tilted head. Tears stung her eyes. I'm so ashamed to have anyone see an ugly duckling like me with my father, she thought. Suddenly her face brightened. She went to her closet and took out a beautiful new cloak. It had never been worn before. Jane smiled, without realizing how pretty her face looked. "Now maybe the children won't notice my crooked back so much."

Jane hurried downstairs. She gaily twirled around in front of her father, who was waiting for her. "How do you like my new cloak?" she asked beaming. "The best seamstress in Freeport made it for me." She always felt happy when she was near her father. He had been both father and mother to her. Her mother had died when she was only a little more than two years old.

"It's the loveliest cloak I have seen, Jennie," her father said. "I am sure it will be much prettier than any cloak the other little girls in the Sunday school will have." He paused. "I'm sorry. I don't think you should wear it. Your old cloak will keep you just as warm and will not make the others feel bad."

Without a word, Jane went back upstairs and changed to her old cloak. She was silent all the way to Sunday school. Just outside the church, she turned to her father and asked, "Why can't the other girls have pretty coats like mine?"

"Things are not equal in this world," her father answered. "Some people are poor, some are rich; some are thin, some are fat. When it comes to clothes and houses, you may not be able to make things come out just right for all. But people should be equal when it comes to the important things in life, like going to school and going to church."

Jane nodded her head slowly. "When I grow up," she vowed, "I will try to make things equal for people."

Not long after, Jane was reminded of the poor people again and how unequal things were in the world. Her father took her for a drive into Freeport. This thriving city of 10,000 was six miles from Cedarville, where they lived. Jane loved to visit Freeport. The toy shop and candy shop were here. Also, the school where her sister Alice and brother Weber went was in Freeport. When she grew older, she would go there, too. But now as they drove along, her father turned down a strange side street she had never seen before.

"Where are we going?" Jane asked.

"I'm taking a short cut," Mr. Adams explained, "to get to the bank before it closes."

Jane was surprised to see narrow, dirty streets and rickety houses jammed close to one another. Once Mr. Addams had to pull the horses in sharply because a group of girls and boys were playing in the gutter. This was a part of Freeport Jane had never known.

"What a pity that they have no real place to play," Jane said. "It must be dreadful to be one of those children."

Jane thought of the beautiful two-story gray brick house to which she would soon return. She thought of the broad fields and rolling hills behind her house where she could roam freely.

Jane tossed her head with sudden determination. "Some day I am going to live in a big house, but it is not going to be built among other large houses," Jane said. "I'll build it right in the midst of horrid little houses like these. I'll invite the girls and boys to come and play in my back yard. I'll serve their mothers tea. I'll invite the fathers for dinner. Maybe then, for a little while, they'll forget about being poor."

Mr. Addams took one hand from the reins and patted the slim girl next to him. "You are a wonderful girl, Jennie. I want you to be well and happy. I do not expect big things of you. But one day, I know, you will do fine things to help people."

"How can I do anything?" Jane sighed. "I'm only a silly girl with a crooked back."

"A girl who gets up at three o'clock in the morning to read is not silly, although you should be sleeping."

"It was so exciting reading *The History of the World,* I just couldn't put the book down."

"Jennie, Jennie, Jennie!" Her father laughed until the tears rolled down his cheeks. "A girl who thinks *The History of the World* is exciting is far from silly. Your back may be bent but your mind is clear and straight. But," her father said, wagging his finger at her, "I wish you would do your reading in the daytime."

"I can't help it," Jane explained. "Sometimes I hear you stirring downstairs when you get up in the morning."

"I'll try to be more careful," her father said. "I didn't know that I disturbed you. I am so used to rising early. When I was a miller's apprentice in Pennsylvania and took my turn at the flour mill, I had to be up at dawn. I can't break the habit."

"I don't mind getting up early," Jane said. "I want to read through every book in the library, just as you did."

Mr. Addams laughed. "Reading is its own reward, but you deserve a special reward. For each volume of Plutarch's *Lives* that you read, I will pay you a nickel. And I will pay you twenty-five cents for every volume of

Irving's *Life of Washington* you read."

"Twenty-five cents!" Jane gasped. "For reading a book!"

Mr. Addams smiled. "You will have to read carefully. I will question you about the books. It is not how many books you read that is important, but how well you read them."

Mr. Addams drew the buggy up in front of the bank. "I'll only be gone for a short while. Here's five cents for the sweet shop."

Jane was just coming out of the candy shop with a bag of lemon drops when she saw her father strolling up the street toward her. He bowed and tipped his hat to several of the ladies and gentlemen whom he passed. Jane drew back. The old feeling of her ugliness returned. But, as her father came up to her, he swept off his hat and bowed deeply. "At your service, Miss Addams. May I escort you home?"

A young lady standing near by smiled.

Jane's face dimpled. Her father wasn't ashamed of her. Why should she be ashamed of herself? She would make her father proud of her. Someday she would be a great lady.

CHAPTER II

• A NEW FRIEND •

"This is my son, George," the tall, beautiful woman said, urging a small boy forward. "You two should get along well," the woman added, turning to Jane, who was standing primly before her in the parlor. "George is just about your age."

"So he is," Mr. Addams smiled. "Jane is eight."

Jane looked at the fine gown the lady was wearing. She had heard Mary and Alice whispering about Mrs. Haldeman. Her husband had died some time ago, leaving her with an eighteen-year-old boy, Harry, and young George.

Jane glanced shyly into the beautiful woman's face. Her sisters had said her father wanted to marry Mrs. Haldeman. Jane wondered how it would feel to have a new mother. Polly was sweet and understanding, but she was only a housekeeper. Mary was gentle and willing to share everything and rubbed Jane's back when it hurt, but she was only a sister. And Mr. Addams said it was about time that Mary was finding herself a husband. It would be nice to have a mother, especially a beautiful mother like Mrs. Haldeman.

"There are lots of things you can show George around here," Mr. Addams said. "Mrs. Haldeman and I are going to have some tea. You and George can go out and play in the fields. But stay close by. Polly will call you in a little while for cookies and milk."

Silently, Jane led the way around the corner of the wide gray house, then back of the barn and out into the green meadow beyond.

George trailed along behind her. Jane didn't know what to do or say. She had never had any friends her own age to play with. She always had to play games by herself. Sometimes she would play in the bins in her father's flour mill, but her only companions were her dolls.

"Would you like to play something?" Jane asked timidly.

George stared at her hard. Jane's cheeks began to grow hot. Oh, he mustn't make fun of her. He mustn't. She did so want him to be her good friend.

"Is anything the matter?" she asked, smoothing back her brown hair, which the wind was gently blowing about her face.

"Why do you hold your head on the side like that?" George asked directly.

Quick tears came to Jane's eyes, but she answered unflinchingly, "I was sick when I

was a baby. My spine became twisted. It makes my head turn to one side."

"You look like a bird when you turn your head that way." George bent down and picked a flower. "Here's a purple windflower for you," he said. "It'll look pretty in your hair."

Jane's heart pounded. No one had ever said she was pretty before.

"Would you like to take a walk along the millstream?" Jane asked, feeling much better now.

"Yes!" George started off eagerly. "It would be fun if I could live here with you. I could watch them cutting the logs in your father's sawmill. I could—" He looked away shyly. "I hope your father marries my mother."

"I would love to have you for a brother," Jane said softly.

"I'll be your knight, Jane. I'll take care of you." George stomped about. "Are there any snakes around here?"

"Oh, yes," Jane said. "I see a few water snakes every time I walk near the river."

"Are you afraid of snakes?" George asked.

"No," Jane said. "They're all God's creatures."

George stopped and picked up a stick.

"I'm going to make a sword out of this and paint it, then if a mean old rattlesnake wants to kill you—"

Jane laughed merrily. "Oh, George, you're silly. I don't think there are any rattlesnakes around here."

"I don't care," George persisted. "I won't let the tiniest bug hurt you." He pointed his wooden stick at the high hills beyond the river. "Have you ever gone exploring up there?"

"When my back doesn't hurt too much, Polly sometimes gives me a picnic lunch and I go up there." Jane lowered her voice. "There are caves up in the hills and there's one great big, inky black one. You can't see anything at all inside. I'm going to take a candle one day and go way deep inside and see what's there."

"Let's go now," George cried, pulling her hand.

"We can't." Jane drew back. "We promised we'd stay close by the house."

"Who cares about cookies and milk?" George asked. "This will be more fun."

"It's not the cookies and milk," Jane explained. "I can't tell my father a lie."

George looked at her. "It's not a big lie. It would only be a small fib."

"It doesn't matter what you call it. A lie is a lie. I remember when I was a little girl, I once told my father a lie. I couldn't sleep the whole night." Jane paused, shivering a little as she remembered that night so long ago. "It was way past midnight, but I got out of bed and ran to my father's room. I woke him up and told him everything."

"Wasn't he angry?" George asked.

"No. He told me that if he had a little girl who told lies, he was very glad that she felt too bad to go to sleep afterwards."

George shrugged. "All right, if that's the

way you feel about it. Let's go back to the house." He paused. "Say, listen, do you hear that whippoorwill?"

"Yes, but why do you know so much about birds and plants when you live in the city?"

"I like studying about nature," George said, "don't you?"

"I never thought about it," Jane said. "I like playing in the hills and gathering black walnuts in the fall but I never really studied about nature."

"Well, if I come to live here, I'll make a butterfly collection for you, and I'll show you all the bugs I've got mounted on sheets of paper."

Jane put out her hand. "I like you, George. You're going to be my very best friend."

Mr. Addams and George's mother did get married and for the next nine years George was Jane's closest companion.

CHAPTER III

• OFF TO BOARDING SCHOOL •

"I hate to say good-by," George said, as the last of Jane's trunks was thumped downstairs.

"It's not good-by," Jane said. "You'll be at Beloit College, only a short distance away from Rockford Seminary. Just think what fun it will be for you to hitch your buggy and come to visit Rockford on week ends. All the girls will love you, I'm sure," she teased.

"Yes, we'll have lots more good times together again," George said. "But things will never be the same."

"Did it really mean so much to you, George?" Jane asked softly.

"You know it did, Jane," he answered.

"Yes," she nodded, "your coming meant much to me, too. Remember how shy we both were nine years ago and now—"

"And now, Jane, you're seventeen, and off to boarding school." He clasped her hand in his. "I wish you would marry me. Look at how happy your sister Alice and my brother Harry are now that they've married."

Jane put her fingers lightly on his lips. "It would be an honor to be your wife, George, but I want to go to college and get a degree." She turned away and walked slowly to the living-room window. She drew back the curtains and gazed out over the fields where George and she had played together so happily.

George followed behind her. "Anything you set your heart on doing, you'll do well," he said. "It's too bad your father wouldn't let you go East to Smith College."

"Father means well," Jane interrupted. "My sisters have all gone to Rockford Seminary, and he thinks it best for me to go there, too. Besides, you know, he's a trustee there. It would look peculiar if I went to another college." Jane smiled wistfully. "I understand the way he feels. He's afraid that I'll be too weak to stand the strain of college and so he wants me close to home."

"You amaze me, Jane. You always are ready to see another person's point of view even if you disagree with him," George said. "But for selfish reasons, I'm glad you'll be at Rockford. I'll have more chance to see you there."

"From what I've heard, I'm going to be quite busy studying. Miss Sill, the principal, is very strict."

Jane was right. College studies kept her very busy. She studied Latin and Greek, science and history, modern languages and literature. But that was only the beginning of her interests.

She enjoyed debating and took a special public speaking course. She liked writing, too, and contributed many articles to the *Rockford Seminary Magazine*. In her senior year, she became the editor-in-chief.

Jane's life at Rockford was not all study. She made many friends. Ellen Gates Starr was one of her best friends. She remained at Rockford only one year, and then left to teach. But Jane and Ellen kept up a long, lively correspondence. Jane wrote Ellen about what she was doing in school, and Ellen told Jane about her teaching experiences.

Jane missed Ellen's companionship very much. But just when she thought she would never again have a close school friend, she met Catherine Waugh. Catherine was a freshman. She had just come to Rockford Seminary.

It was a nasty, rainy day, but one of the rules of the school was that all students had to walk an hour each day, no matter what the weather.

Catherine was splashing along in the rain, muttering to herself, when Jane passed by.

Jane waved to her. "I see you're new here," she called. "Miss Sill allows the students to walk on the boardwalk around the buildings when the weather is very bad."

Catherine shook herself like a wet puppy. "You'd think I was the Pony Express and had to get the mail through. Do you girls really walk in snow and—"

Jane laughed. "After a while, it's fun."

"Fun!" Catherine snorted. "I'd rather study Greek."

"Would you really?" Jane asked. "I love Greek. Miss Blaisdell is helping me read the Greek testament."

Catherine smiled. "At least I can study Greek indoors."

Jane put out her hand. "I'm sorry I didn't introduce myself right away. I'm Jane Addams," she said.

"I'm Kittie Waugh. I know that we're going to be good friends."

As the days passed, Jane and Catherine found out they had many interests in common. But the thing that excited Jane was the fact that Catherine wanted a college degree as much as she did. Both of them believed that Rockford Seminary should become Rockford College. Both of them were willing to take difficult, advanced courses to prepare themselves for a B.A. degree.

One afternoon, as they were sitting in Jane's room, working on a tricky calculus problem together, Kittie snapped her book shut. "It's not fair!" she said, jumping up. "It's just not fair!"

"Whatever are you talking about?" Jane asked.

"Here we are working and working, studying the same subjects as your brother George and the other men at Beloit College, but are we going to have our work recognized? No! We're women and so—"

"Now don't get excited, Kittie," Jane said calmly. "The thing for us to do is to stop talking and start acting."

Kittie pounded her fist on the desk. "But how?" she said. "How?"

A chance soon came their way by which they hoped to put Rockford on the same basis as other colleges in the state. Jane and Catherine asked to be allowed to compete in an intercollegiate oratorical contest to be held in Jacksonville. Up till then the contest had been restricted to men's colleges. After much waiting and suspense, Rockford was finally admitted as the first woman's college. Jane was given the honor of representing the Seminary, and Catherine was chosen as her alternate. But as hard as she tried, Jane only placed fifth in the contest.

"Oh, the girls will be so disappointed," Catherine said, after the debate was over. "I feel as if I have personally struck a blow against women's rights."

"Don't be foolish," Jane laughed. "The boys were just better than we. Did you hear that boy, William Jennings Bryan, from Illinois College? I would have voted for him myself, he spoke so well. And Rollin Salisbury, George's good friend at Beloit, was as good as George boasted he would be."

"No matter what," Catherine sighed, "the girls at school are going to feel terrible."

"Well, if you're unhappy about going back right away, how would you like to visit the state institution for the blind, as long as we're here? And then there's a wonderful school for the deaf and dumb. They're doing some interesting work, I read in the newspapers, teaching youngsters."

"How do you do it?" Catherine asked admiringly. "Always thinking of others."

Jane smiled. "It is only by thinking of others that we think of ourselves. It is only by giving to others that we may receive."

"Jane, you seem so sure of yourself. What do you want to be when you graduate? I'm going to study law and be a lawyer. I want to help women get the vote. It's unfair that women should not be allowed to vote."

Inequality again, Jane thought, a cloud passing over her face. "I think I should like to study medicine and live with the poor," Jane finally said. "I'm going to register at the Woman's Medical College in Philadelphia. George is planning to study at Johns Hopkins University in Baltimore. We won't be too far away, so I'm sure that this time I can convince father to allow me to go East to study."

As the time for Jane's graduation neared, Miss Sill called Jane and Catherine into her office. "So far you are the only two young ladies who want a college degree," she said somewhat reprovingly. "If you graduate with your class now, Jane, you can only receive a certificate. We are not yet set up to give degrees."

"But that's not what I want," Jane burst out. "I'm sorry for interrupting you, Miss Sill," she apologized, biting her thin lips, "but I have all the qualifications for a B.A. degree."

"That is so," Miss Sill nodded, "and our charter states that Rockford can grant a college degree, but we have never done so before. I cannot see the value of a college degree for girls. You should devote yourself to a life of service to God." Miss Sill looked appraisingly at Jane. "You are a clever girl, Jane.

You could do well with foreign missions. You know I am keenly interested in training my girls at Rockford to go into this field. I regard it as the most worthy one there is."

Jane swallowed hard. Her words came out slowly. "I would like to train myself for a life of service to man, and the more I know, the better. Besides," and her voice rang out clearly in the principal's office, "that is not the main question, Miss Sill. It is a question of inequality."

"Inequality?" Miss Sill frowned. "What nonsense are you talking about?"

"There is no reason why a girl who studies the same subjects as a boy and earns the same grades, if not higher, should fail to get a college degree."

Miss Sill looked at the frail, tense figure before her. "As you can understand, it takes time to work out official details and legal matters; but if you insist, next year you will receive your B.A. degree from Rockford College."

"From Rockford College," Jane murmured under her breath, tears of joy blurring her eyes. "Thank you, Miss Sill. Thank you so much."

The principal stood up, puzzled for a moment, then put out her hand. "No. Thank you, Jane. You may be more right than I."

Jane graduated in June, 1881, with a certificate. A year later she returned to Rockford and received her precious B. A. Later on, she was to receive many honorary degrees, but Jane always felt a special thrill about this first degree for which she had worked so hard not only for herself, but for all girls interested in higher education.

CHAPTER IV

• SHATTERED DREAMS •

After graduation, Jane wondered whether she was right in signing up for medical training. She wanted to do something useful. She wanted to help people, but she didn't feel certain she could succeed as a doctor. As she always did when she had a problem, she turned to her father.

"Do you think it wise for me to go East for medical study?" she asked her father one afternoon, in early August, as they were strolling in the garden.

"I don't know whether you'll be a good doctor or not, Jennie," he said. "It is not easy for a tender woman like you to see so much pain and misery day after day, especially when you are not very well yourself. But I do know that you'll try your best."

A few weeks later, Jane recalled that conversation with tears in her eyes. Her father had died suddenly from an attack of acute appendicitis.

"Perhaps you should forget now about going off to Philadelphia," her mother urged. "It will be lonely in the house without you and George."

"No, now I must go more than ever. If we knew a little bit more about appendicitis and other ills, just think how many lives could be saved. Maybe one day I can help save some father's life for his daughter."

But this dream was not to be for Jane. After studying at the medical college for seven months and receiving excellent grades, Jane fell ill. Her spine was so weak that she had to be taken to the hospital. It was only after many weeks that she was finally allowed to go home.

Day after day passed. Jane felt low in spirits. Her mother hung Jane's diploma on the wall in front of her bed so she could see it each morning when she awoke. She hoped it would rekindle Jane's enthusiasm. But what good was her hard-won college degree, Jane felt, when she was chained to a sick bed? It was just as she had said to her father. She was still a silly girl, and there was nothing for her to do.

Jane's mother didn't know what to do to shake Jane's depression. Then one morning after Jane had hardly touched her breakfast, Mrs. Addams came upstairs with a thin package of letters. On the top was a slip of paper in her father's handwriting saying: "Mr. Lincoln's Letters."

"It might do you good to think of a man—two men—who never gave up," Mrs. Addams said, handing Jane the letters. "Abraham Lincoln and your father."

Mrs. Addams closed the door softly behind her and left Jane alone. "Abraham Lincoln and your father." How wonderful for those two great men to be linked together! Jane remembered how ably her father had served Illinois in the state senate for sixteen years. He had had a chance to be governor, too, but had turned it down, preferring the quiet life at Cedarville.

"Perhaps he could have been president," Jane whispered, as she opened the top letter. She smiled at the way the letter began: "My dear Double-D'ed Addams." Mr. Lincoln always had a good sense of humor.

Jane shifted uncomfortably in bed. If only her father were here to guide her. Mr. Addams had known Lincoln quite well before he became president. The two men had exchanged many letters. Jane lifted her head proudly. Mr. Lincoln was very interested in Mr. Addams' views on how to run the government.

Jane thought of the pictures of Lincoln that hung in her father's room, and she remembered the one of Lincoln with his son Tad in the upstairs parlor. All of a sudden, Jane had an overwhelming desire to see this picture again. She had been awed by it as a child. It was not many steps from her bedroom to the parlor. Surely she could make it. Slowly she swung her feet off the bed. A sharp pain shot through her back and her head fell back limp. But a moment later, she propped herself up. "I will not spend the rest of my life in bed," she said aloud, almost angrily. "There is too much to be done. I will get up. I will get well."

Her mother flung the door open before Jane had walked halfway across the room. "I heard what you said just now, Jane, and you

are right. I have wonderful news from Harry. Alice and he want you to come to Mitchelville and stay with them for a while."

"But how can I," Jane asked despairingly, "when I'm sick?"

"Harry has been doing a good deal of research about spinal injuries such as yours ever since he became a doctor. If you agree, he's willing to operate on you. He thinks there's a chance."

"Oh, Mother, Mother," Jane said, throwing her arms around Mrs. Addams, "when do I start?"

For six months after Dr. Harry Haldeman operated on her spine, Jane stayed with her sister Alice in Iowa. Her recovery was slow, but Jane never complained.

"I'm beginning to feel like a permanent boarder, Dr. Harry," Jane said one morning at breakfast. "I ought to pay you rent."

"I wouldn't worry about that," Dr. Harry said with a broad wink. "If I were a good fortuneteller now, my crystal ball would predict a long ocean voyage for you."

"Oh, Harry, you've gone and given her the secret," Alice protested.

"What secret?" Jane's pale cheeks became pink with excitement.

"You might as well tell her," Dr. Harry said. "Mother will be here in a few days."

"For a visit?" Jane asked.

"No," Alice laughed, "to spirit you away to Europe, no less."

"Do you think I'm up to it?" Jane asked hesitantly.

"With your spirit, Jane, you're up to anything," Dr. Harry assured her. "I think a change of scene will do you good. And your father always wanted you to go to Europe."

On August 22, Jane and her mother sailed on the "Servia" for England. "I'm going to keep a diary of this trip," Jane told her mother. "It's going to be the most wonderful experience of my life."

And it did turn out to be a wonderful adventure. For two years, Jane and her mother traveled all over Europe. They went to England, France, Holland, Germany, Austria, Italy and Greece. Jane went to dozens of art galleries; attended scores of concerts and operas; and studied German, Italian and French, until she could speak the languages like a native. Day by day, her diary grew bigger and bigger. But every once in a while, as she wrote, she would lift her pen, a thoughtful, puzzled expression on her face.

She couldn't erase the memory of the night she and her mother had been taken on a tour of the slums of East London. Crowds of beggars had gathered to buy left-over, rotting fruits and vegetables. By law the produce could not be sold on Sunday and it would not keep until Monday. She couldn't stamp out of her mind the sight of one ragged, old man who had been able to buy a head of cabbage. He sat down on the curb as soon as he got it and bit into it, dirt and all, gulping it down as if—

And then Jane would black out the memory. It was as if her thinking had reached a dead end.

But the vision haunted her. She would stand in front of a famous painting in a museum and suddenly it would fade and she would see the upraised hands of the poor, begging for a penny's worth of rotten food.

One evening Mrs. Addams came in to find Jane in a reverie, her diary open before her. "Can't think of anything to say?" her mother laughed. "You should have come to the theater with me this evening. The performance was superb. The—"

Jane lifted her head suddenly. "Mother, I want to go home," she said firmly. "I'm wasting my time here."

"Do you call traveling through Europe, learning about some of the finest culture, wasting time? Why, Jane, you have enriched your life."

"For what purpose?" Jane cried out. "What am I being educated for? To do nothing?"

"What is it that is bothering you, Jane dear?" Mrs. Addams asked gently, surprised at Jane's determination.

Tears glistened in Jane's eyes. "I've got to go back to America. I can't enjoy this luxury any more, knowing that somewhere in America there are slums like those in East London."

"But Jane, you are a young girl, tenderly raised. What can you do?"

"I don't know yet. That's the terrible thing. But somehow, someday, I will find my way."

CHAPTER V

• THE MOMENT OF DECISION •

Jane was at home during 1885 and 1886, but she found nothing to which she could devote her time and energies. But the summer of 1887 her friend Ellen had saved enough money from teaching to go abroad. Her letters to Jane were so enticing that finally Jane, restless and bored, decided to join her. She persuaded another friend, Sarah Anderson, to go to Europe with her.They sailed on December 14, 1887.

"Perhaps mother is right," Jane said. "Maybe there is still a good deal which Europe can give me."

The three friends met in Rome. Ellen was

studying art, and Jane decided to study about early Christianity. Her studies were abruptly dropped, however, when she fell ill again. "You and Sarah must travel on without me," Jane insisted. "I won't spoil your trip for you. You have waited for it too long. I will join you as soon as I am able."

But it wasn't until the spring that Jane was well enough to travel. Her friends were now in Spain, and she joined them there.

"Have you seen much of Spain yet?" Jane asked her friends.

"No, we were planning to see a bullfight this afternoon," Ellen said. "You know, when in Spain do as the Spanish do."

But when Ellen saw the first bull killed, she felt upset and left the amphitheatre.

"I think I'll join her," Sarah declared a few minutes later, her face growing pale as she watched the picadors prod the second bull. "Coming, Jane?" she asked.

Jane shook her head slowly, as if she were in a dream. When she finally joined her friends, Ellen and Sarah stared at her in astonishment.

"How could you have sat through that—that awful sight?" Ellen asked in amazement.

"Ellen, this may sound strange," Jane explained, "but after a while I didn't see the bulls in the ring. I sat in a daze. I saw knights of old, battling for what they believed to be a just cause."

"Is it just for the bulls to be killed?" Sarah broke in, still horrified by what she had seen. "I simply can't understand how the Spanish enjoy this sort of thing."

"That's the point, Sarah. There are so many things we don't understand. Can you understand why the early Christians were willing to be thrown to the lions rather than give up their faith?"

"Well, they had such a strong belief—" Sarah began.

"You're right. They believed in love, but they also believed in action. The poor bull driven in the ring cannot save himself from death, just as many people, driven by poverty, cannot save themselves from the meanness of life unless—" Jane's eyes glowed with a new light. "Ellen, I'm through with idleness. At last, I know what I'm going to do. I'm going to rent a fine house right in the middle of ugly houses, and then we'll open our doors and our hearts wide to the poor. Over the entrance door I'm going to have carved 'May you find hope who enter here.' "

"Why, that sounds something like Toynbee Hall," Ellen said.

"Toynbee Hall?" Jane wrinkled her brow. "Where is that?"

"I'm surprised you haven't heard of it," Ellen said. "Toynbee Hall is a settlement house in the East End of London among the very poor people."

"East End," Jane echoed. "How I remember that place! I shudder when I think of it."

"It is a dreadful section of London," Ellen went on. "That's why Arnold Toynbee felt it a good idea for young men from Oxford and Cambridge University to go there and live among the poor. He wanted to learn about the poor people and their ways by being a part of them."

"That's just what I had in mind," Jane said, growing excited. "I will go to London at once and find out all I can about this idea. If highly educated men and women in England can dedicate their lives to living among the poor, why can't we?"

"We?" Ellen echoed.

"Yes, *we*, Ellen. Can I count on you to be one of the first to help me start a settlement house in America? We will be pioneers in a new field. America has always been a land of opportunity and challenge. This is our opportunity and challenge. Will you accept it?"

"I would never forgive you if you didn't let me share in it," Ellen smiled. "You can count on me, Jane."

At last Jane had found her purpose in life. She went to Toynbee Hall in London. There she spoke to the director, asking for his ideas on how she could help the poor. She spoke to the workingmen and women who came to Toynbee Hall. She listened and learned how she could start a settlement house of her own. Then she returned to the United States and set her affairs in order. At last she was free to find a place to start her new venture.

But where to start? There were poor people all over.

"New York might be a good place," Ellen suggested.

"Yes," Jane agreed, "but I would like to be

closer to mother now that the family is so scattered. Weber is married and has a farm not far from Ann Arbor. Alice and Harry are still in Iowa—"

"Then what about Chicago?" Ellen interrupted. "If ever there was a city that needed help, Chicago is it."

"Yes," Jane mused, "I had been thinking seriously about Chicago myself. So many foreigners are coming to Chicago now. They tend to stick together in groups. They are a part of America, and yet apart from America. We could start in a small way by being friends with these poor immigrants."

"It sounds wonderful," Ellen said, feeling more and more excited.

"I have long thought," Jane went on, "that one of the saddest things for these people who have left their homelands is to arrive in a new, strange country without friends. A strong man, willing to work, can soon earn money. But it is not easy for the same man, who knows little English, and who is afraid of our ways, to make friends. Yes, the more I think about it, the more I feel that Chicago is the answer."

For months Jane went trudging through Chicago's slums, looking for just the right house, in just the right neighborhood, where she could do the most good for the most people. But she couldn't find what she was looking for.

One day a real estate agent agreed to take Jane house-hunting once more through the crowded foreign section of Chicago. "We've been through this neighborhood several times before," the man said wearily, stumbling over a pile of rags and papers that had been dumped on the sidewalk. "You won't find anything here."

They were turning down a side street when, through a narrow alley, Jane spotted an old, rundown, two-storied, brick house.

"That's my house," Jane said suddenly. "It's just perfect."

"Perfect for what?" the real estate man groaned. "It is in the middle of mud, misery, and mice. There are many better buildings I can show you."

Jane hardly heard him as she turned her gaze eastwards to the river. "Over there is the Italian section," she said, waving her slim hand. "And here, along Blue Island Avenue, is the Bohemian section."

"Not to mention the Germans, the Poles, and the Russians up the side streets," the man laughed. "Now why would this particular area interest you?"

"Look around you. The unpaved alleys interest me; the garbage in the streets; those poor children playing near the ash cans; the houses crowded together, with no fire escapes—"

The real estate man shrugged. "The house you want is the old Hull House. It used to be beautiful. But it's gone to ruin now. Part of it is rented out for tenements; part is used to store furniture."

"It can be beautiful again," Jane said, as they went up Halsted Street to the house.

"I'll see what I can do, if you're really interested. Mr. Hull died and left the house to his cousin, Helen Culver."

"If you explain to the lady what we want the house for, I'm sure you'll have no trouble getting her to agree to rent the house to us."

Jane was right. Helen Culver rented Jane the second floor, and a small part of the first floor. This was all the space that was available at the time. But not long afterwards, Helen Culver gave Jane a free lease to the entire house.

CHAPTER VI

• HULL HOUSE BEGINS •

On September 18, 1889, Jane, Ellen and Mary Keyser, a housekeeper, moved into Hull House.

As each load of new furniture arrived, as the pictures and precious chinaware were carried into the house, the neighborhood men and women gathered together into curious groups to watch.

"I used to be a wood-carver in the old country," a German baker said. "The chair that was just brought in is made of the finest mahogany I have ever seen."

"And did you see that magnificent engraving of Albrecht Durer's *St. Hubert?*" an

Italian woman, with a hand-woven shawl over her head, asked. "She can't mean to hang it in that house. It will rot on the walls."

"Haven't you seen them scrubbing, polishing, and cleaning?" a French woman put in. "As if they could get rid of all the dirt around here!"

"Do you know that the tiny, thin one was sweeping the street this morning?" an Irishman laughed, as he passed by.

"Well, I guess that proves they are crazy," the German baker shrugged. "You can tell from their gowns that they are fine people. Why would they want to live here?"

The curious onlookers were so busy watching the furniture go into the house that they hadn't noticed Jane coming slowly up the street behind them.

"We want to live here," Jane said with a smile, pausing before going into the house, "because we want to be friends with all of you. *Guten Morgen,* Herr Schmidt," Jane held out her hand to the baker.

"You know German," Mr. Schmidt said in great surprise. "And you know my name," he concluded, in still greater surprise.

"I bought some bread at your bakery yesterday morning, and I saw you then," Jane explained. "I hope to know all of you soon. You are all invited to visit us. I hope that you will allow me to come to visit you. You would be doing me a great favor."

The door opened then, and Ellen came out. "I was going to look for you," she said. "I was afraid that you might have gotten lost or something might have happened to you. But," she added with a smile, "now that I see you safe and sound, I would like to take advantage of this goodly gathering to announce that beginning next week we are going to have a reading party. The book will be George Eliot's *Romola.*"

Jane watched as the news was passed back and forth among the women. Would they come, she wondered? And if they came, would they enjoy it and want to come back again?

"Two members of the reading club will be invited for dinner each week," Jane added, "as our guests."

"I will tell my daughter to come to your reading party," one woman called out excitedly. "She has no money to buy books but this—this sounds like a dream."

It all seemed like a dream to Jane, too, in the beginning. But gradually news about Hull House, as the settlement house came to be known, spread. The curious came to stare and stayed to help.

A kindergarten day nursery was started almost immediately. Jenny Dow, one of Ellen's friends, came to see what her friend was doing in Hull House. She was touched by the little ones who were left at Hull House because their mothers had to go out to work. Jenny took them to heart—and took over the running of the kindergarten.

Jenny became so enthusiastic about the work being done at Hull House that she, in turn, persuaded one of her good friends to come to Hull House. Mary Smith, like Jenny, fell under the influence of the wonderful spirit that prevailed at Hull House and she soon found her special place in its work. Since Mary loved music, she started music clubs to teach music to girls and boys who could not afford lessons. But that was only a beginning for her. She helped out in the art studios when they were shorthanded. She pitched in when the Boys' Club needed an extra helper. And that still was only a beginning. Mary gave generously of money, as well as time, when Hull House sorely needed both.

Jane was delighted to get the help of these eager women, but help was not enough. She lacked the money to carry on the many activities that kept multiplying with each day. Afternoon clubs had been started for girls and boys who had no place to play after school. Evening classes and concerts were given for mothers and fathers who could not pay for recreation.

Jane hoped one day to find a fairy godmother for Hull House who would bring it some of the ever-needed funds. Louise Bowen was the answer. Mrs. Bowen was a wealthy Chicago woman who had heard much about the work at Hull House. She decided to drop in one afternoon. Her one visit turned into many visits. Before long she was one of Hull House's most ardent supporters. She joined the Hull House Woman's Club and soon became president, an office she held for almost seventeen years. Under her leadership, the Woman's Club which had started out as a meeting of mothers for the purpose of self-improvement grew into an active group for civic and social betterment.

But no matter how many people offered to

help, no matter how hard Jane worked, there always seemed to be more to do. In time, Jane went out lecturing. She thought it important to explain the work that she was trying to do at Hull House. Her old love for debating and public speaking served her well then. But as good as her ideas were, sometimes she saw them run into a dead end because of lack of money. She poured as much of her own money into Hull House as she could, but there never seemed to be an end to poverty. In the morning, another new ragged child would appear at the door, hoping for a bite to eat. In the evening, a working girl whose eyes were bleary from sewing in one of Chicago's sweatshops would find relief and beauty by attending one of Ellen's classes on art and art appreciation.

"How can you talk to these women about art?" asked one wealthy man, who was touring Hull House with Ellen. "Most of them don't have a cent in their pockets. How can they think about art, when they should be thinking about food?"

"They may be poor in material things, but they are not poor in spirit. Their souls are rich with beauty," Ellen replied.

"I see," said the man. "I never quite thought of it that way."

A week later, the man was back. "I'm Mr. Butler," he said, introducing himself to Ellen. "You may have heard of my business in Chicago."

"Mr. Edward Butler?" Ellen blushed. "I did not realize who you were when I spoke to you."

"I don't think it would have made any difference," he said, smiling. "I would like to ask you to do me a favor. Would you please ask Miss Addams if I may make a gift to Hull House?"

"Why, thank you, Mr. Butler. Any small

amount you can contribute will be most welcome. There are always so many children to be cared for. We would like to build up our arts and crafts program. A few dollars—"

Ellen wondered if she might suggest twenty-five dollars or more. After all, Mr. Butler was a very wealthy man.

Mr. Butler's smile broadened. "I was thinking of having Hull House build an art gallery," he said smoothly. "A place where the poor could come to see art exhibits, and perhaps a studio room in which they could paint and—"

For a moment, Ellen was too overcome to speak. "Mr. Butler, you must forgive me if I've lost my manners and my voice," she finally gasped. "I cannot say more than thank you. Your greatest thanks will come from those who will benefit from your generosity. And now if you will excuse me—" Her feet flew. She was bursting with the news. She ran into Jane's room. "Jane, Jane, we're on our way."

Jane looked at Ellen's shining eyes, her flushed cheeks. "You look as if you're on the way to the moon. Do sit down and calm yourself."

"Nothing can stop us now. Hull House is growing. We have just been given a gift of our first building."

CHAPTER VII

• THE WORKING CHILDREN •

But not all businessmen were like Edward Butler, as Jane and Ellen were to discover to their dismay. Many Chicago businessmen looked upon Jane and her Hull House project with anger.

"She's always up to something," a department store manager grumbled.

"I don't trust her," a factory owner added. "My workers who attend her Hull House classes are always coming here and complaining. They say that the factory is dirty; we don't have enough windows. They say the machines they work on need safety guards. I know how to run my business. I don't like interference, especially from a thin, scrawny woman who looks like a chicken!"

In time these remarks came back to Jane. They made her sad. But they did not stop her. Jane was learning a good deal about her neighborhood. And most of what she learned was not good.

To people in Europe, the United States in the 1890's seemed like a land of opportunity. The lands in the Far West and the Northwest needed settlers. The railroads were calling for more and more men to build miles of track across the nation. Factories advertised for thousands of workers to turn out clothes and tools and goods of all kinds. Things looked good in the United States to the poor peasant toiling in Germany, to the shoemaker in Italy. They saved their money and came to America. Many of the immigrants planned to go West. Many of them did. But a good many of them were caught up in the Midwest. Chicago was a city bursting at the seams. Chicago's population had more than doubled in the ten years before Jane came to Hull House. Almost three-fourths of the people in the city were foreign born.

The men and women who came from Europe to America were eager to build a new life for themselves. They gladly took whatever work was offered to them. They were grateful for the opportunity to earn a few pennies. But as more and more immigrants arrived, there was less and less work for them to do.

In desperation, families sent their children out to hunt for work. Many of them found it: in damp basements; in sweatshops where there was no air; in rickety lofts, where the floors creaked, and death lurked around the corner if a fire should break out.

Jane Addams had heard a little about child labor. But she did not really understand what it meant until Hull House gave its first Christmas party.

"I am going to send to Freeport for some of the licorice sticks and molasses jawbreakers that I used to love as a child," Jane said to Ellen, as she pushed a table against the wall. They had just finished moving the furniture around in the first-floor drawing room to make space for the Christmas tree.

"The children will love the candy no matter where it comes from," Ellen panted, exhausted from hanging the decorations and moving the furniture around. "They see so little of sweets."

Jane, Ellen, and Jenny Dow, the kindergarten teacher, were all puzzled as child after child refused the tempting plates of candies they passed around.

"Perhaps you have never seen candies like these," Jane said bewilderedly, popping one into her mouth. "Taste one. It's delicious."

"I'm sick of candy!" one little girl sobbed suddenly. "Take them away."

One of the mothers, who had offered to help at the children's party, drew Miss Addams aside. "Please forgive the children," she said. "They do not want to spoil your party, but you see during the holiday season many of them have been working. They have been spending fourteen hours each day in a candy factory, for six days a week. You can hardly blame them if the sight of candy makes them sick."

Weakly, Jane staggered over to a chair. "The idea of children ten years old or younger working in a factory for—oh, my, the whole idea makes me sick." She looked up at the women. "Why doesn't someone do something about this? Why can't it be stopped?"

"How can it be stopped?" the woman shrugged. "The few pennies the children bring home can often mean the difference between starving and living. Often the little ones can get jobs more easily than their fathers."

"But that is not living!" Jane was on her feet, her thin hands clenched. "I will do something about it myself."

But trying to get decent working laws for children was a big task. Luckily, just when Jane needed help, Florence Kelley and Julia Lathrop, who had come to live at Hull House as "residents," were able to supply it. Both of these young women felt as Jane had when she first started Hull House. Both were well educated and wanted to do something useful with their education. Julia had studied law. And as soon as Jane told Florence about the disgraceful conditions for working children in Chicago, she, too, studied law so that she would know the best possible way to wipe out child labor.

Jane, Julia, and Florence investigated and discovered that there were no laws protecting children in factories. They went to see businessmen, politicians, and labor leaders. Finally, in 1891, a law was passed which prevented the employment of children under thirteen in stores, shops, and factories.

"I feel like celebrating," Jane said, when she heard this law had been passed.

"Not so soon," Julia warned. "We'll have to see if it's going to work."

Julia was right. Although the law had been passed, no way had been set up to make the employers follow it. Most employers simply ignored the law.

But Jane was not to be discouraged. "If this law doesn't work, then we must fight for another law that will work. I want children to be children, not old men and women before their time."

Florence Kelley took up the problem and spent countless wearying hours trying to work out a fair solution. Finally a new and much better law was passed in 1893. Florence Kelley was appointed chief factory inspector to see that the law was obeyed this time.

"Who is this Jane Addams and her friends that they think they can tell us how to run our business?" many factory owners complained. "Not allow children under fourteen to work —humph! Restrict the working day for women to eight hours! Why, we'll be ruined."

"I'll go out of business before I'll follow that law!" one plant owner grumbled.

One after another, big businessmen began to tell the governor that he must change the law.

"It's unconstitutional!" they declared. "The law is taking away our rights."

When a new governor was elected, he removed Florence Kelley from her job. But that was not all. The law that women were only allowed to work eight hours was declared unlawful and illegal.

Florence Kelley didn't want to go to Hull House the night the news broke that the law had been declared unconstitutional but she didn't count on Jane's fighting spirit.

"The people are not ready for this law now," Jane said. "They must be educated to realize how important it is. I don't blame the businessmen who think I am ruining their business. They still don't see clearly that they are ruining human lives, and that is what I must teach them."

At long last, on July 1, 1903, a wonderful law went into effect in Illinois. It improved conditions for the child who worked and protected other youngsters from going to work at too early an age. Jane ended her battle with a sigh of victory and happiness.

CHAPTER VIII

• THE JANE CLUB •

Jane tried out many new things in Hull House. But she was always ready to change any of her own plans if she found that the people in the neighborhood were not interested. At one time, the idea came to her of having a public kitchen in Hull House. Here inexpensive soups, stews, and other good foods would be sold to working women who did not have time to make nourishing meals. But the women in the neighborhood preferred their own style of cooking. When Jane saw that the public kitchen was not what people wanted, she dropped the project.

She was delighted, then, when a wonderful

idea came from a group of working girls who met at Hull House. As they always did when they had a problem, the girls came to Jane.

"Miss Addams," one of the girls announced, "we have gone out on strike at our shoe factory. Do you think we did right?"

Jane hesitated. "I can't say. I only know that most strikes result in cruelty and waste. I would rather see the workers and employers sit down together and work out their differences. People can't reach a fair and just settlement when they're angry."

"But you don't know how horrible conditions were," the girl protested. "Scraps of leather were left rotting on the floor. There's no ventilation in the room, no place to work. There are rats."

"Conditions were as bad as that?" Jane asked.

"Worse, if the truth were told," another girl put in. "The owner could clean up a little if he wanted to, but it wasn't only that!" The girl's eyes flashed. "I'm used to working like a slave in the middle of filth and dirt, but he wanted to cut our wages. We're making little enough now. I'm glad we're out on strike. If we can only stick together." She wheeled around suddenly, pointing to a small dark girl, huddled in one corner. "But that one! She's ready to go back, and we've only been out a few days."

"I can't help it," the girl retorted, her lips trembling. "The rent is due at my boarding-house. If I don't pay the landlady by to-morrow, she threatens to put me out. I have no family, no place to go."

"You know you can always come here," Jane said kindly.

"That's not the point," the girl argued, coming forward. "Many of us are afraid to go on strike. We know that we'll be thrown out of where we live if it lasts too long."

"I hate to agree with her," a blond girl cut in, "but she's right."

"Don't say you hate to agree with anyone," Jane said. "But now that you know the problem, what can you do?" This time she did not ask, "What can I do?" She felt that the girls could work out their own problems, and they did.

"We can start a co-operative boarding club," one of the girls suggested hopefully. "If we can share living together, we needn't be afraid, at any time, strike or no strike." The girls hugged one another with joy. "And you will help us, won't you, Miss Jane?" they chorused.

"Help I will," she said, "but this must be something of your own."

And so the Jane Club was started. On the first of May, 1891, two apartments were rented near Hull House and fifteen young women moved in. The Club thrived. Within three years, they had taken over six apartments and had fifty members.

The Jane Club was doing so well that they needed more apartments. Jane promised to help the girls get a new building for themselves. But where was she to get the money? Hull House was already hard pressed. The music school was going strong; the boys had a good gymnasium in which to play, but they always could use more sports equipment; the drama group needed costumes for the shows they put on.

And then Mary Smith came forward as she had many times before.

"Jane," she said, "a friend of my father's who knows of my interest and love for Hull House has offered to give twenty thousand dollars for you to build the new club house."

"Twenty thousand dollars from a stranger!" Jane was overcome. "Now I know how Ellen felt when Mr. Butler made his offer to build us the art gallery. I am stunned. To whom are we indebted?"

"Oh, you know this man quite well, I'm sure," Mary said. "He's—"

When Jane heard the man's name, her face clouded. She bowed her head silently. When she finally lifted her head, her face was gray with anguish. "We can't accept the money,

Mary. Go thank your friend. But the girls have told me too many stories about him."

"Stories?" Mary asked, distressed.

"Yes, he underpays his workers. He makes them work extra hours, without paying them. He—" She shook her head hard as if to toss away the ugly sight. "But enough. It's not easy for me to say no, but I could not build a club house with money that came from a man like that. You cannot build good on evil."

It took a while longer, but finally the Jane Club succeeded in building a new and beautiful club house.

CHAPTER IX

• A PLACE TO PLAY •

"Money, money, money!" Jane murmured to herself one afternoon as she walked home from a meeting. She had been invited to explain the settlement movement, which was now spreading across the country, and whenever she spoke she felt keenly how much more needed to be done.

An excited youngster, using a long stick for a bat, hit a wild ball. It went sailing through the air and knocked off Jane's black silk hat.

"Quick, scoot!" his friends called, and a few of the boys ran into the back alleys and hid.

But the boy who had hit the ball knew Jane. He picked up her hat and dusted it off. "I'm sorry, Miss Addams," he said. "We like to play ball. I'd like to be a good baseball player one day, but there's no place to practice except here in the street."

"It is I who am sorry," Jane replied. "I've been thinking so much about children who have to work, that I have not paid any attention to the children who have no place to play."

How could children play in dirty streets? No wonder the boys ganged together and often got into trouble. There was nothing for them to do, nothing to occupy their time.

Jane went into Hull House thoughtfully. She sat down at her desk, her heart heavy. She picked up a letter from her sister Mary. But even the welcome news about Mary's growing family couldn't lift her spirits. A short while later, Julia Lathrop found Jane still sitting, staring into space, her hat still upon her head.

"What are you dreaming of now?" Julia gently teased.

"I have been thinking of my home in Cedarville—the sun-filled fields, the flowers, the wind as it rustled through the pines. I have been thinking of—"

"How different it all is from Hull House," Julia ended for her.

Jane sighed. "Yes. It's one thing to try to take the children out of the factories, but what good will it do us to throw them into the street? What good will it do to give the children time if they can do nothing but get into mischief? We've got to give the children a chance to play, and a place to play."

"What about our clubs? The dramatics club, the art school, the—"

"I mean a place to play outside in the sun."

Just then, there was a rap on the door.

"The door is open," Jane called out. "We never close the door at Hull House."

In stormed a red-faced man. "I'm William Kent," he roared. "Which one of you is Jane Addams?"

Julia smiled. "This will probably be the only time in my life that I'll say I'm glad I'm not Jane Addams. If you'll excuse me, sir," she said, bowing her way out, "I'll leave you with Miss Addams. It looks as if you have a problem."

"I don't have a problem," he shouted. "You do."

"All problems are better if they are explained when seated," Jane said politely. "Do sit down."

Somewhat abashed, Mr. Kent sat down. Jane looked at him steadily. "Well," he fumbled, his eyes falling, "I'm sorry for barging in this way, but one of your residents just gave a speech on housing reform in which I was accused of—of—some pretty unspeakable things." He jumped up excitedly. "I won't stand for it. I'm a decent person. I'm no worse than any other landlord. Why should I be singled out and insulted?"

"You must understand that I am not responsible for the opinions or speeches of our residents, unless they concern Hull House matters. But I'm sure no insult was intended," Jane said sweetly, standing up. "The block of tenement houses you own is right near here. Have you seen them recently?"

"Of course not. I have an agent who collects the rents and—"

Jane smiled. "Since my hat is on my head, perhaps you would like to take a stroll and see what your tenants, and your tenement houses, look like."

"Now, look here," he blustered, "I didn't come here to—"

"But this is property you own," Jane said

firmly. "Perhaps it is time you saw it."

Without another word, Mr. Kent followed Jane down the street. "Here are your houses," Jane said, pointing to a few sagging, broken-down wooden houses as they passed.

A little boy came running up the street and bumped into Mr. Kent. "Watch where you're going, you dirty thing!"

"This house has no water in the apartments," Jane said calmly. "There is a faucet in the back yard. Some of your houses have no sanitary facilities, either," she added. "It's not easy for a youngster to go out and wash himself in the back yard in the winter time."

"I—I lost my temper again," he apologized. "I'm sorry. This whole thing has unnerved me. I'm not a bad man, Miss Addams," he said. "I had no idea how terrible things were here. I've never been down here." Suddenly he whipped out a handkerchief and covered his nose.

"That's just the odor from one of the many stables on this block," Jane said. She looked at Mr. Kent hard. "If I were you, Mr. Kent, I would use that clean white linen handkerchief to cry into, instead of covering my nose."

"What do you want me to do, Miss Addams? I'll do anything you say."

"The property is yours, Mr. Kent. Look it over well. You must decide." With that she turned on her heel.

In two weeks Mr. Kent was back at Hull House. This time his face was glowing. "Miss Addams, I'm going to give you the property, free and clear, to do with as you please. It's your problem, not mine. Now let's see what Hull House will do with the houses."

"You have made a very generous offer, Mr. Kent. The rent from the houses would help us carry on our work here. But Hull House will do nothing with those houses, if we are the owners, but destroy them. We cannot allow people to live in them. Those houses are dangerous. As you saw, many of them have no fire escapes. We cannot take the property unless you pay to have the houses torn down."

"Pay to have the houses torn down!" he sputtered. "What good will the property be then? An empty lot is no good. It does not bring in any income, and taxes will still have to be paid on the land."

"An empty lot is good for a playground," Jane said. "A place where boys can run without running into obstacles. A place where children can throw a ball without running the risk of being knocked down by the wagons that pass."

Mr. Kent threw up his hands. "I give up, Miss Addams. I bow to you in defeat."

"No, in victory," she said, putting out her hand.

"I will do whatever you wish."

The houses were torn down, and the land was cleared. On May 1, 1892, the first public playground in Chicago was opened.

But Jane Addams never stood still. As she solved each problem, she saw another before her.

CHAPTER X

• THE NEW AMERICANS •

In the 1890's, and well into the twentieth century, Hull House was surrounded by a "Little Europe." Through Jane's gentle guidance and example, through coming to the clubs and getting to know one another, many men and women of different nationalities, who had thought of themselves as enemies, became fast friends.

Jane found that love and understanding could cut across all national boundaries. But there was one problem that disturbed her greatly, and she didn't know what to do about it. Many of the young girls and boys who came to America were eager to become

Americanized as soon as they could. They went to school. They learned to speak English. They studied and worked hard. They wanted to forget about the old customs and traditions they saw at home. They didn't want to be known as "Tony, the Italian," but "Tony, the American." It was with deep heartache that Jane saw the girls and boys snub their parents; taunt and make fun of their European clothes and ideas.

"I must do something," Jane said, when Louise Bowen dropped in to see her one afternoon, "so these young Americans won't be ashamed of their immigrant parents. I want them to be proud of America, but I want them to be proud of their parents, too. I know how much I loved my father. If it hadn't been for him—"

"If you hit upon an idea," Louise promised, "I'll help you all I can. Now put on your hat and take a walk in the sunshine. Mary tells me you've been shut in here all day working on another article."

"Yes, so many people misunderstand what we are doing that I must do my best to make our position clear."

In later years, Jane was to write eight books to make her position clear on various subjects but now she was paving the way with her articles.

Jane took her hat down from the closet shelf, put it on, and followed Louise into the morning sunshine.

"My, but it does feel good to be out," Jane said, stopping to breathe deeply. "I didn't notice how quickly time was passing. Spring is in the air. There are no flowers here, as there were in Cedarville, but I can feel spring anyway, creeping up these city streets."

At Polk Street, Louise and Jane parted. Jane wandered on a bit longer, enjoying the balmy day. As she passed an old tenement, she saw a stooped, Italian woman sitting on the front steps, a spindle in her hand.

"*Buon giorno,*" Jane greeted her.

The old woman looked up and smiled. "Good morning to you, *signorina.*" Not many young American women spoke Italian. She waved to Jane to come over. "Come, look," she called haltingly, "see what I am making." She held up her spindle.

"*Molto bene,*" Jane complimented her.

"*Grazie, signorina.* I am making a pair of stockings for my granddaughter, Rosa. In the store, the stockings are made by machine. These," she touched the colorful yarn lightly, "are made with love."

"They are lovely," Jane said, but her mind was no longer on the woman. A new idea was beginning to bud in her mind, just as the trees and flowers were beginning to bud. What if the old people could be persuaded to come to Hull House and do spinning, fine embroidery, sewing, needlework, weaving, wood carving, metal craft—wouldn't the children be proud then? Wouldn't they realize what a precious heritage, what a wonderful background, their parents had? Perhaps the old folks couldn't speak English well, but their nimble fingers could translate wood into a statue, clay into a fine pipe, wool into a shawl, bits of cloth into a bedspread.

"*Arriverderci,*" Jane called good-by to the old woman. She went flying back to Hull House. The first person she collided with on the steps was Ellen.

"I've got it!" she exclaimed. "I've got it!"

"What? Money for another building?"

"No, something more important I think. An idea to bring a closer understanding between our crop of new, young Americans and their parents."

Ellen was twice as enthusiastic as Jane when she heard about the idea. "But there

is more to it than that," she said. "Wait and see. This idea is going to grow and grow."

Ellen was right. The idea mushroomed. It all started with one room in Hull House, which was set aside for those in the neighborhood who were skilled in some particular craft.

Ellen was fired with enthusiasm. "Do you know that if we could gather together different kinds of spinning wheels and some weaving machines, we could show these youngsters how modern industry has developed. Perhaps they'll understand more about the machines they are working on at the factories if they learn to appreciate the humble beginnings of these tools."

"Let's concentrate on people, and not on tools," Jane suggested.

But surprisingly, the little exhibit that Ellen prepared of textile machines aroused great interest.

Ellen scoured the neighborhood, adding,

bit by bit, many different kinds of textile tools, until she had a fine exhibit. From this small beginning sprouted the idea of a Labor Exhibit, and finally a Labor Museum. And now it was Mrs. Bowen's turn to help. Her husband built a large building, called Bowen Hall, on Polk Street, not far from where Jane had first seen the Italian woman spinning. Here there was room for many things besides the exhibit of working tools. There was space to accommodate all of the Boys' Clubs, an auditorium where meetings and concerts could be held, and finally a shop was opened where the handicrafts turned out by the European immigrants were sold.

But it wasn't the dollars and cents value of this project that counted for so much. It was the rich feeling of pride that the young people began to take in the work of these older men and women that was important.

CHAPTER XI

• WOMEN'S RIGHTS •

Jane had much to occupy her at Hull House but she always found some time to visit her sisters and her nieces and nephews. It was a deep grief to her when in July of 1894 her sister Mary died. Her sister left her youngest child, a boy of ten, to Jane's care. Jane regarded the boy and his older brothers and sisters as her special family.

"I will have the boy come live with me here at Hull House," Jane told Ellen. "He will have a chance to see the city and get to know Chicago."

"Is it fair to the boy?" Ellen asked. "Hull House is Chicago and everything to you."

"Well, we'll leave it up to him," Jane said.

But the decision was not left up to the boy. When the boy came to Chicago for a visit, Jane had her family physician check him. After his examination, the doctor turned to Jane. "The boy is in perfect health but he won't stay that way long if you keep him here."

"I don't understand," Jane said puzzled.

"How can you take this child away from a clean, healthful life in the country and drag him into this filth?" the doctor demanded. "Do you know how many new cases of typhoid and tuberculosis there are in this area each month? He could catch a dozen diseases from the children here." The doctor mopped his brow. "Forgive me for speaking so bluntly, Miss Addams, but I know that you have your nephew's best interest at heart. Send him away, as far away from Hull House as you can, if you want him to live."

"If it is not safe for my nephew to live here, then it is not safe for the other children to live in this neighborhood, either. Have I become blind to the dirt and disease around us?" she pondered.

Early the next morning, Jane took a walk up Halsted Street. The courtyards were crawling with vermin. The streets were covered with refuse. As she turned up Polk Street, she saw a decayed heap of fruits and vegetables. "The East End of London is coming back to haunt me," she whispered to herself. "I have not succeeded in my purpose. It is a fine thing to make Hull House an oasis, but what meaning can it have if we are living in the midst of such filth and do nothing to stop it?"

Stop it. But where to begin? she asked herself. She tripped over a rusted can, which had spilled out over a dirt-filled wooden box. It was fastened to the sidewalk to hold gar-

bage. Suddenly Jane stopped. Garbage, that was it! That's where she could begin.

As she always did, Jane did things thoroughly. She began a careful investigation of the city's system of garbage collection. The Hull House Woman's Club helped her. The women went out and discovered in the Hull House neighborhood one thousand and thirty-seven violations of the health laws during August and September alone. In the spring of 1895 when the city contracts were awarded for the removal of garbage, Jane put in a bid for the garbage removal in her district.

"This is a man's job," Mary protested. "You cannot be serious."

"Good health is everybody's job," Jane answered. "I'm not interested in politics. I'm interested in saving the children in our neighborhood from sickness."

At that time Chicago was divided into thirty-four wards. There were two aldermen in charge of each ward. They were supposed to look after the health and welfare of the people who lived in their ward. But sometimes the aldermen were too busy with other matters—such as making money—to be concerned about the conditions in their ward.

To her great surprise, Jane was made garbage inspector of the ward, with a salary of a thousand dollars a year. Jane took her job very seriously. She got up at six o'clock each morning to see that the men were at work on time. She followed the loaded garbage wagons to the city dump. She insisted that the number of garbage wagons be increased.

"She's a nuisance," the garbage wagon contractor grumbled. "Let's give her her way, and then we'll hear no more from her."

But when Jane got only nine instead of thirteen wagons for her ward, as she had requested, she kept on asking for more until she finally had seventeen wagons removing garbage. As usual, Jane did her job well. The death rate in the ward dropped. It became possible to walk in the streets without stumbling over refuse at every step. Jane did her job so well that the alderman who was in charge of the ward had her job eliminated by a trick. It was decided to put a "ward superintendent" in charge, a position for which only men were eligible.

Mary was furious when she heard the news. "I didn't want you to take on the extra burden of the job at the beginning, Jane, but now if the mayor doesn't do something about this at once—"

"Don't be so upset, Mary," Jane soothed. "The job itself was not important but what the job accomplished. I do feel, though, that this incident proves another point. We must work as hard as we can to get women the vote so that women can hold all kinds of government jobs." She handed a letter to Mary from her desk. "I've just heard from my old friend Catherine Waugh. She's devoting her full energies to fighting for the right of women to vote. I have promised her that I will get in touch with her soon to help in whatever way I can."

"But, Jane, where will you get the time?"

"I don't know," Jane said, smiling, "but the more things I do, the more time I find to do things."

And so Jane joined another battle. First she was made vice-chairman, then later chairman of the Women's Clubs Committee for Municipal Suffrage for Women. It was a very impressive title, and a very impressive job. She was placed in charge of more than a hundred different women's organizations, all of them interested in and working for the right of women to vote. Again Jane took to the lecture platform and spoke in behalf of what she believed right. She published articles and a book explaining why she believed in woman's suffrage. The book was called *A New Conscience and an Ancient Evil.*

This was another battle that took many long years of hard work. Finally in 1913 a bill was passed in the Illinois state legislature giving the women in Illinois the right to vote for the president of the United States and for all city and state officers, unless these positions were limited to the votes of men only. It was not until 1920 that the Nineteenth Amendment was passed by the United States Congress, which gave women throughout the United States the right to vote.

CHAPTER XII

• TRIUMPHS AND TRIBUTES •

The years came and went, the seasons came and went. Spring turned into summer. The hot sun began pouring down on the city streets.

One afternoon in July, Jane and Louise Bowen passed the Kent playground and noticed that it was almost empty.

"Where are the children?" Louise asked.

"It's too hot for them to be at the playground in this weather. It would be so nice if they could have a place in the country, a place of their own."

"A country club," Louise laughed, "just like the millionaires."

"Why not?" Jane asked seriously. "Why can't the Hull House children have a country club?"

And in 1912 the children of Hull House did get a vacation resort, which was just as wonderful to them, if not more wonderful, than the most luxurious hotel that a millionaire could go to. Mrs. Bowen, in memory of her husband who had died, had the Joseph T. Bowen Country Club built. It was on seventy-two acres of land, not far from Chicago, overlooking Lake Michigan. Jane was thrilled. Here were hills such as she had known in Cedarville. Here were flowers and trees and water. Here, too, were houses and cabins and a boys' camp. She tried to see that each member of Hull House spent some time there each summer, at least one week end, and many children were able to enjoy a two weeks' vacation at the club.

"If it weren't for you," Jane said one summer's evening, as she and Louise drove to the Country Club, "many city children would never have seen tomatoes growing in a garden. They would never have had the fun of picking raspberries in season, would never have known the beauty of a sunset on the lake."

"No, Jane," Louise said, "if it weren't for you."

Jane was happy with the way Hull House had grown through the years, yet she was not content. Jane believed that just as people of many different races in her neighborhood could learn to live peacefully side by side, nations could learn to live peacefully together.

For many years Jane had been working actively in behalf of peace. In the 1900's Jane Addams was prominent in all the important peace conventions that met.

Then in 1914 World War I broke out.

"You will have to change your views now,"

Mary Smith said to Jane one evening, when she came back from a church meeting where she had spoken out against war.

"Never!" Jane declared.

"Everyone agrees that war is horrible and stupid," Mary went on. "Innocent people are hurt. But now that it is here—"

"To me the worst thing is that war prevents people from getting to know one another, from understanding one another," Jane said. "If we could only find this mutual basis of love and understanding, there would be no further need for war; no further need for me to speak against it."

"They are saying ugly things about you, Jane," Mary said sadly. "If the United States ever gets into this war against Germany, they will accuse you of not being a good American."

"I cannot go against my conscience," Jane said firmly. "I have had doubts about many things I have done in my life. It took me a long time to find a course in life, to start Hull House. But I do know this. War is wrong."

But Mary's fears turned out to be true. When the United States entered World War I against Germany, and Jane still talked out against war, many of her friends drifted away. The newspapers called her a traitor. Some men and women stopped coming to the Hull House clubs and meetings.

In spite of her beliefs, Jane did serve her country in its time of war, although many people did not know of her work. During part of 1917 and through 1918, Jane worked for the government's Department of Food Administration.

"I may be against war," she told Mary Smith, "but I am not against humanity."

Jane realized, as she had when she came to Hull House, that people had to be fed bread before they could be fed ideas. In 1922 she published a book on the work done by herself and other women pacifists. This book was called *Peace and Bread in Time of War*.

When the war was over, Jane's interest in peace grew stronger. With women from many of the European countries, including former enemy countries, she helped to form an organization called the Women's International League for Peace and Freedom. For fourteen years Jane presided at each of these Congresses. When Jane finally resigned in 1929, she was elected honorary president for life. She had carried so much of the work on her own shoulders that after she resigned, no new president was elected. Instead, three chairmen were appointed to carry on in her place. But it would take more than three people—or a hundred, or a thousand—to take Jane's place, or fill her shoes.

She was a unique woman in American history and social thinking. She was awarded fifteen honorary degrees and many awards. In 1910 Yale offered her an honorary degree, the first honorary degree Yale had ever given a woman. Smith College, which she had yearned to attend, made her an LL.D. But as the awards and prizes accumulated, she still treasured that simple hard-earned B.A. degree from Rockford College.

Finally, in 1931 Jane Addam's efforts in behalf of peace were internationally recognized. She was awarded the Nobel Peace Prize. She immediately turned around and gave the money she had received to the Women's International League.

"At least, keep some of the money for yourself," Mary Smith urged.

"How can I, Mary?" Jane asked. "The prize is not for my work, but for the good work the League is doing. I am only the instrument by which this still, small voice of peace will not be silenced."

Jane took these honors that rolled in year after year in the same quiet, dignified way that she had accepted her defeats.

Each day found her at Hull House whenever she was in Chicago, seeing people and listening to problems, as she had done at the beginning. And now she had taken on a new task. She was writing a biography of her good friend, Julia Lathrop, now dead, who had meant so much to her.

In 1935 Jane was seventy-five years old and going along as spry as ever. Dr. Alice Hamilton, who had come to Hull House as a resident in 1898, had taken Jane under her wing since she saw how hard she drove herself. Although no one ever heard Jane complain about her back, Dr. Alice knew how much pain it still caused her, and how many sleepless, tossing nights she spent. Now in January, Dr. Alice took Jane aside.

"As your friend, as your doctor, Jane, I

must insist that you cut down on your work. It is too much for you."

Jane smiled. "There is still so much to be done, Alice. You know that as well as I. Work will never kill me. It will have to wear me out."

Nothing and nobody could stop Jane Addams. In February, 1935, she was given the American Education Award; in March, she received an honorary degree from the University of California. It seemed that everyone now was anxious to show their appreciation for the great work of a great woman. But the best was yet to be. The Women's International League was celebrating its twentieth birthday. In Washington a huge celebration dinner was being planned in honor of Jane. It was given on May 2, at the Willard Hotel ballroom, with over a thousand people present. Many more hundreds, who had come to pay her tribute, had to be

turned away since there was no more room.

Millionaires—such as Gerald Swope, president of General Electric Company, and people who represented the workingman, such as Sidney Hillman, president of the Amalgamated Clothing Workers of America, came to honor her. This pleased Jane more than anything. If people could sit down together, they could live together.

Mrs. Eleanor Roosevelt, wife of the President of the United States, came to pay honor to Jane. She said, in her tribute, "When the

day comes when difficulties are faced and settled without resorting to the type of waste which war has always meant, we shall look back in this country upon the leadership you have given us, Miss Addams, and be grateful for having had you living with us."

Jane was thrilled by the dinner and the warm words of praise, but when she got her chance to speak, it was not about herself but about peace. She felt the world still had a long way to go before achieving this glorious ideal. Quietly, yet firmly, her head bent to one side, as it always was, she said slowly so that all the world might hear. "The worst thing about war is not the poison gas which wipes out lives and destroys cities, but the poison it spreads in the minds of man. We must educate the people to fight the spread of this poison."

After she left Washington, she returned to Chicago and her work at Hull House. One morning she complained of a severe attack of pain. Jane was rushed to the hospital. She never saw Hull House again. She died on May 21.

Presidents and princes, scrubwomen and society women, sent messages of condolence. Chicago planned a tremendous funeral. But the people in the nineteenth ward, those who still lived there and those who had lived there but had moved away, set up a clamor, "Jane Addams belongs to us." And so arrangements were made for her body to lie at rest in Bowen

Hall. Fifty thousand people came to pay Jane Addams their final respects—Irish, Poles, Greeks, Russians, and people of other nationalities; factory owners who had been factory boys when Hull House started; bent seamstresses, who had sent their children off to college and a better way of life in America; children who had been given new hope and new heart by Jane. She had scrubbed their faces and shined the fading light in their souls. Fifty thousand of them came, and no words could express their grief. No tears could wash away their deep loss.

One of Jane's young nieces standing in the courtyards, surrounded by the people who came and came and came, in an endless line, turned curiously to ask her mother, "Are all of these people Aunt Jane's family?"

Before her mother could reply, an old Italian woman patted the little girl's head and said gently, "Yes, my dear, we are all Aunt

Jane's family." And that would have been the greatest tribute—the greatest honor—that Jane Addams would have wanted.

They took her home to Cedarville, where she was laid to rest beside her beloved father. A simple marker was put up that said:

Jane Addams of Hull House
and the Women's International League
for Peace and Freedom

That was all that needed to be said.